# CARCASSI

## Classical Guitar Method

### CONTENTS

## CARL FISCHER®

65 Bleecker Street, New York, NY 10012

ISBN 0-8258-0049-8

# Rudiments of Music

Before the student commences to play any musical instrument it is advisable for him to become acquainted with the rudiments of notation.

Music is written on or between five parallel lines, called the staff:

The symbols indicating the pitch and duration of the different musical sounds are called *notes*.

There are seven natural tones in music, named after the first seven letters of the alphabet in the following order: C, D, E, F, G, A, B. These seven tones are repeated from the lowest to the highest register.

To determine the name and pitch of the notes, a sign called a *clef* is placed at the beginning of each staff. There are several clefs. The music in this book is written in the treble (or G) clef placed on the second line of the staff and naming that line G.

The names of the lines and the spaces in treble clef are as follows:

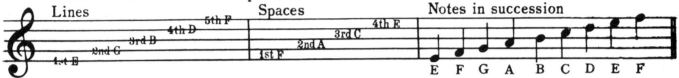

The above notes are not sufficient to cover all the tones of the instrument's full range. For this reason it becomes necessary to go above and below the staff with the aid of short added lines, called leger lines.

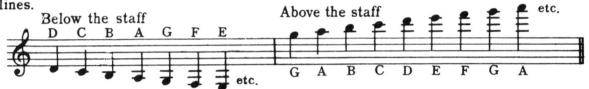

The time value of a note is shown by its form: o whole note, ♩ half note, ♩ quarter note, ♪ (or in groups ♫ ♫♫ ) eighth note, ♬ (or in groups ♬ ♬♬ ) sixteenth note, etc. The duration of a note is measured by beats or counts.

## COMPARATIVE TABLE OF THE RELATIVE VALUE OF NOTES

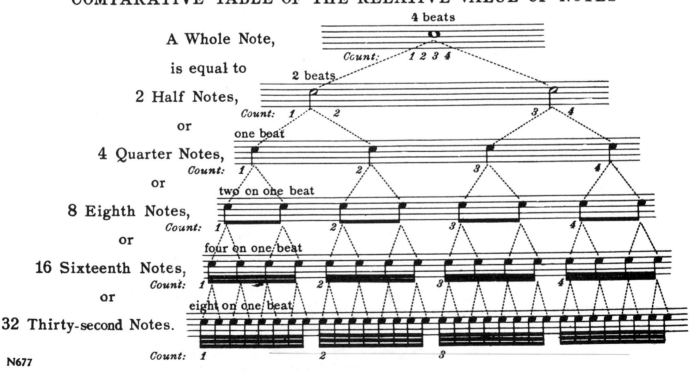

A Whole Note,

is equal to

2 Half Notes,

or

4 Quarter Notes,

or

8 Eighth Notes,

or

16 Sixteenth Notes,

or

32 Thirty-second Notes.

# RESTS

The symbols indicating silence are called *rests*. For every note there is a corresponding rest having the same time value, as shown below:

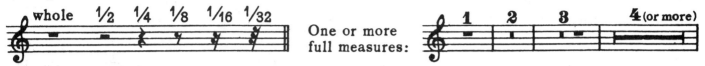

Written music is arithmetically divided into measures by bars drawn across the staff. Each measure contains the same time value. How many beats each measure shall contain is deter - mined by the time signature placed after the clef, (²⁄4, ³⁄4, ⁴⁄4, ³⁄8, ⁶⁄8 etc.), The top number gives the number of beats in each measure and the lower number suggests the kind of note that is to receive one beat, i.e. ²⁄4 means two beats to the measure, one beat on each quarter note.

The time signature most frequently used is ⁴⁄4 or common time, also marked **C**. This time signature indicates that each measure contains four quarter notes or their equivalent.

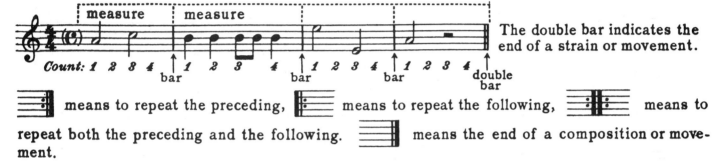

The double bar indicates the end of a strain or movement.

means to repeat the preceding, means to repeat the following, means to repeat both the preceding and the following. means the end of a composition or move- ment.

## ACCIDENTALS

A *sharp* (♯) placed before a note raises it by a half step. A *flat* (♭) placed before a note low- ers it by a half step. A *natural* (♮) restores a note previously affected by a sharp or flat. These symbols are called *accidentals* and they affect all the notes on the same line or space throughout one measure only.

Example:

## KEY SIGNATURES

When the tonality requires that certain notes be sharp or flat for a considerable number of meas- ures or throughout a composition, the sharps or flats are grouped together at the beginning of each staff, forming the *Key Signature;* they affect every note of the same name throughout the compo - sition or until a change is indicated.

Example:

## INTERVALS

An *interval* is the difference in pitch between two tones, in other words the distance from one note to another.

In the above example the intervals are counted from C, the root of the natural scale, but they may be counted from any note.

# SCALES

A *scale* consists of seven consecutive notes between any note and its octave, separated by intervals of 5 whole-tones (major seconds) and 2 half-tones (minor seconds). There are two kinds of scales, major and minor. Counting upward in the *major scale*, the half-tones are between the 3rd and 4th degrees and between the 7th and 8th degrees.

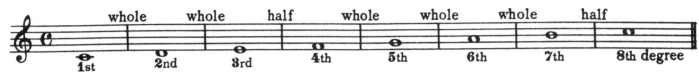

Starting the major scale on any other note it will be necessary to either raise or lower some of the notes to make the half-tones fall between the 3rd and 4th and between the 7th and 8th degrees.

Following this procedure on every note within an octave, we will have twelve major scales, with key signatures as follows:

## THE SLUR AND TIE

The *slur* (⌒ ⌣), a curved line drawn under or over two or more notes of different names, indicates that these notes must be played smoothly (legato) without any cessation of vibration. When this sign (⌒ or ⌣) connects two notes of the same name it indicates that the first note is to be sustained for the value of both. In this case the sign is called a *tie*.

## THE DOT

A *dot* to the right of a note or rest increases its value by half, and each succeeding dot increases the value of the preceding dot by half.

## THE DYNAMICS

The varying and contrasting degrees of intensity or loudness of tones are indicated by signs or letters of which the following are those most frequently used:

*f* = *Forte:* loud

*ff* = *Fortissimo:* very loud

*mf* = *Mezzoforte:* medium loud

*mp* = *Mezzopiano:* medium soft

*p* = *Piano:* soft

*pp* = *Pianissimo:* very soft

◁ or cresc. = *crescendo:* the intensity of tone or tones is to be gradually increased.

▷ or decresc. = *decrescendo:* the intensity of tone or tones is to be diminished.

dim. = *diminuendo:* decrease the intensity.

*sf* or *sfz* = *sforzando* or *sforzato:* give a sudden emphasis to the note.

# THE TEMPO

The tempo indicates the pace of the piece or movements, usually written above the staff at the beginning:

*Largo  Adagio* = very slow
*Andante* = slow
*Andantino* = medium slow
*Moderato* = at a moderate rate of speed
*Allegretto* = medium fast

*Allegro* = fast
*Vivace* = lively, quick
*Presto* = very fast
*Meno mosso* = slower
*Più mosso* = faster

Modifications of speed inside of one or more measures are indicated by:

*Ritardando (rit.)* = gradually diminishing the speed

*Rallentando (rall.)* = same as above

*Accelerando (accel.)* = gradually increasing the speed

The last three markings are usually followed either by a change in tempo or:

*A tempo* = to play at the previous speed

The *Fermata* or *Hold* (⌢) above or below a note means that it is to be sustained beyond its indicated value at the discretion of the player.

Some other commonly used musical terms or marks:

*Da Capo (D.C.)* = from the beginning

*Fine* = the end

*Dal Segno (D.S.)* (𝄋) = repeat from the sign, usually as far as the Fine, or as far as the Coda sign (⊕), then skip to the appended ending of the piece, marked *Coda*.

*Appoggiatura* – grace note or notes preceding the melody note:

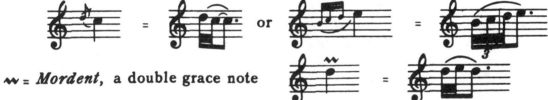

ᴡ = *Mordent*, a double grace note

∞ ᴄᴏ = *Gruppetto* or *turn* is a group of four notes consisting of the principal note with its upper and lower neighboring notes.

Example:

*tr* = *Trill*, is a rapid oscillation between the written note and the note above:

M.M. stands for Maelzel's Metronome, a time beating device, indicating the tempo of the composition. For example, M.M. ♩ = 60 means that when the slider of the pendulum is set at 60, there will be 60 ticks per minute, one for each quarter note or its equivalent.

# MINOR SCALES.

Every major scale has its relative minor, the root of which is to be found on the sixth degree of the major scale. Both scales bear the same signature. There are two kinds of minor scales, the Harmonic and the Melodic, of which the latter form will now be explained.

The ascending and descending form of the melodic minor scale is not alike, the former having its sixth and seventh degrees raised by accidentals not essential to the Key. In ascending, semitones occur between the second and third, and the seventh and eighth degrees; and in descending between the sixth and fifth, and the third and second degrees.

## SCALE OF A MINOR.

without signature, relative to C major.

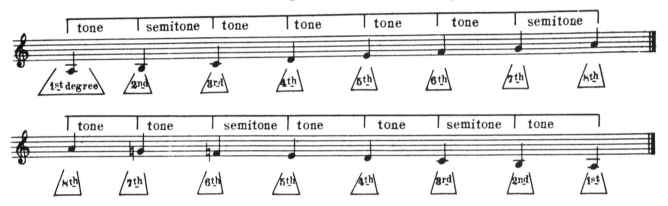

## TABLE OF MINOR SCALES WITH THEIR RELATION to MAJOR.

# THE DOUBLE SHARP.

When a double sharp (✗) is prefixed to a note the note is raised a whole tone. Thus F double sharp will sound like G natural.

# THE DOUBLE FLAT.

A double flat ♭♭ prefixed to a note, lowers the note a whole tone. Thus B double flat will sound like a natural.

## THE LEGATO OR SLUR, THE TIE AND SYNCOPATION.

These three terms are indicated by a curved line, connecting several notes.

With this we understand several notes formed in succession by a single vibration.

Slurred notes.

The Tie indicates that the notes should be held for their whole value, as far as the sign extends.

Tied notes.

## SYNCOPATED NOTES.

Syncopation is the binding of the unaccented part of a measure with the accented part of the measure following, so that in both form one note.

## INTERVALS.

The distance between two sounds is called an Interval.

Unison. Second. Third. Fourth. Fifth. Sixth. Seventh. Octave.

## THE PAUSE.

This sign ⌒ placed over a note, means that the note can be sustained to an indefinite length, at the performer's pleasure, the counting being interrupted.

## ABBREVIATIONS.

To abbreviate is to represent several notes by a single one, or by a single sign.

for    for    for    for

for

Or instead of repeating a single bar a sign marked thus ⅞ is used.

## THE HARMONIC MINOR SCALES.

The harmonic minor scale differs from the Melodic, as only the seventh degree is raised by an accidental, which remains, whether ascending or descending.

## EXAMPLES.

A Minor.    E Minor.

## DIFFERENT SHADES OF TONE.

*p* means: *piano*, soft.

*pp* means: *pianissimo*, very soft.

*f* means: *forte*, loud.

*ff* means: *fortissimo*, very loud.

*mf* means: *mezzoforte*, moderately loud.

*cresc.* or ⎯⎯◁ means *crescendo*, increasing the sound.

*dim.der cresc.* ▷⎯⎯ means *diminuendo, derescendo*, diminishing the sound.

*sf, rf* means *sforzando, rinforzando*, sharply accentuated.

*fp* means: *forte-piano*, loud and immediately soft again.

2435-124

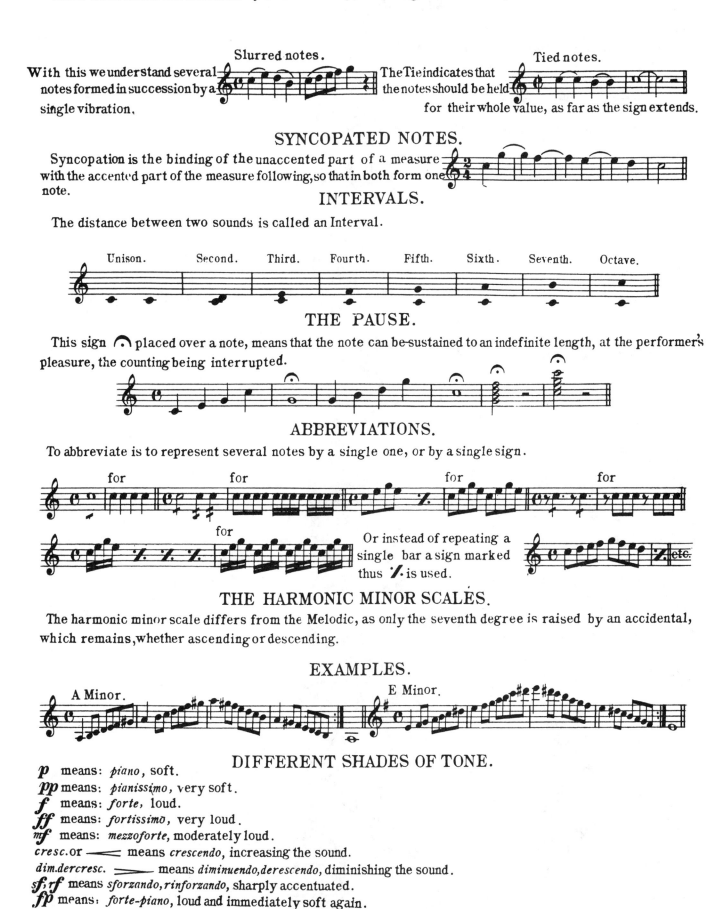

# DIAGRAM OF THE FINGERBOARD OF THE GUITAR

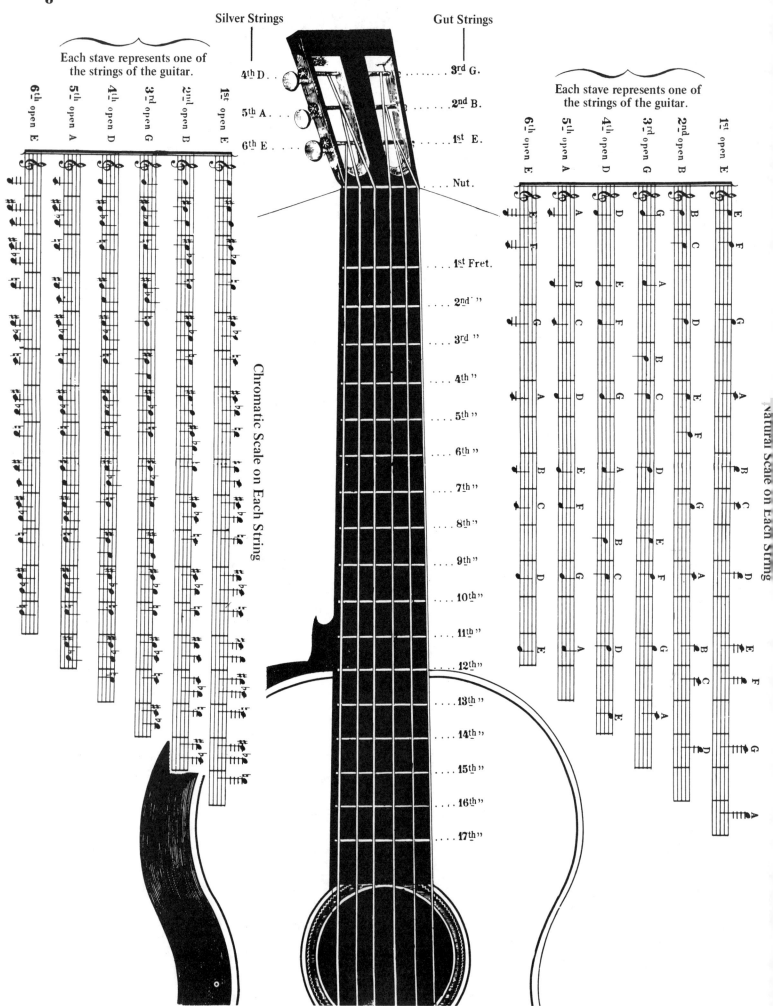

Silver Strings

Gut Strings

Each stave represents one of
the strings of the guitar.

Each stave represents one of
the strings of the guitar.

4th D . . . . . . . . . . . . . . . . 3rd G.

5th A . . . . . . . . . . . . . . . . 2nd B.

6th E . . . . . . . . . . . . . . . . 1st E.

. . . . Nut.

. . . . 1st Fret.

. . . . 2nd "

. . . . 3rd "

. . . . 4th "

. . . . 5th "

. . . . 6th "

. . . . 7th "

. . . . 8th "

. . . . 9th "

. . . . 10th "

. . . . 11th "

. . . . 12th "

. . . . 13th "

. . . . 14th "

. . . . 15th "

. . . . 16th "

. . . . 17th "

Chromatic Scale on Each String

Natural Scale on Each String

# General Instructions

## MANNER OF HOLDING AND POSITION OF HANDS

The guitar has six strings. The first three are spun gut or nylon and the others are covered with thin wire. They are tuned in fourths with the exception of the third string, which is tuned a third below the second. The actual pitch of the guitar is an octave below its notation.

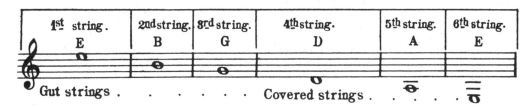

To hold the guitar well it is necessary to sit a little higher than usual. The left foot should rest on a stool the height of which is proportioned to the seat. Place the right leg forward, drawing back the foot a trifle. The left leg should retain its natural position, and the weight of the instrument should rest principally on the left thigh, on which the guitar is placed transversely. This position is preferable because if offers three points of support for the instrument and balances it so that the support of the hands is not required. If there is no stool available, cross the left leg over the right and balance the guitar as above. If it is necessary to play in a standing position, a properly adjusted shoulder strap supports the instrument.

## THE LEFT HAND AND ARM

The left hand should press the neck lightly between thumb and forefinger. The tip of the thumb should rest on the side next to the sixth string, between the first and second frets, and the large joint of the forefinger between the nut (the end of the fingerboard) and the first fret, on the side next to the first string. The arm should hang naturally, the elbow away from the body, and the forearm and wrist should be curved, with the fingers spread and held like hammers ready to stop the strings between the first four frets. In this position the fingers will naturally fall upon the first three strings. When they are required to reach the other strings the wrist should be still more curved and the thumb placed further under the neck. As the hand proceeds higher up the fingerboard the thumb assumes a position further behind to provide additional leverage. The thumb is sometimes (though rarely) used to stop the sixth string for certain notes. This is indicated by the word "thumb" placed under the notes.

## THE RIGHT HAND AND ARM

The right forearm should rest on the edge formed by the side of the instrument and the soundboard, in the direction of the bridge. The thumb should be extended and held over one of the covered strings. The other fingers should be slightly curved and held over the gut (or nylon) strings. The nearer the hand is to the rosette, the softer the tone.

## MANNER OF TOUCHING THE STRINGS

The strings are plucked with the thumb and the first, second, and third fingers. The sixth, fifth, and fourth strings, on which the bass notes are most frequently played, are usually plucked with the thumb. The other three strings to which the melody and passage work are assigned, are usually plucked by the first and second fingers alternately, changing the fingers on each note. The third finger is most often used in chords and arpeggios, but is sometimes used in passage work in alternation with the second finger. While not indicated later in the text, it will be found profitable to play some scales and exercises both ways, i.e., with alternation of first and second fingers, and with second and third.

To obtain a full and mellow tone, apply some force at the tops of the fingers, but avoid touching the strings with the nails, except for special effects. The fingers meet the strings obliquely causing them to vibrate across the fingerboard. The thumb, when plucking the covered strings, should slide to the next string and rest upon it, and should not be removed until required to pluck the next note, except when the next string is to be plucked by another finger immediately, in which case, the thumb should pluck the string without touching any other.

In some cases it is necessary for the thumb to pluck the higher strings, and for the fingers to pluck the lower strings. See examples on top of the next page.

## TUNING THE GUITAR.

An A tuning Fork is used in tuning the Guitar, to which the 5th string, A, is tuned; then press the finger on the same string at the 5th fret of the finger board, which will then give D; to which the 4th string is to be tuned in unison. The finger is then to be placed upon the 5th fret of the 4th string, which will give G, to which the 3rd string is to be tuned in unison; then place the finger upon the 4th fret of the 3rd string, which will give B, to which the 2nd string is to be tuned in unison; place the finger on the 5th fret of the 2nd string, which will give E, to which the 1st string is to be tuned in unison. The 6th string, E, is then to be tuned to the 1st E string, but at the distance of two octaves lower.

### EXAMPLE.

| 5th STRING. Open, 5th fret. | 4th STRING. Open, 5th fret. | 3rd STRING. Open, 4th fret. | 2nd STRING. Open, 5th fret. | 1st STRING. Open. | 6th STRING. Open. |
|---|---|---|---|---|---|

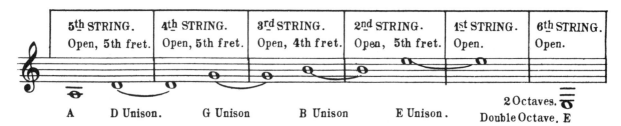

A    D Unison.     G Unison     B Unison     E Unison.     2 Octaves. Double Octave. E

After having tuned the Guitar it is well to prove it by sounding the following Octaves.

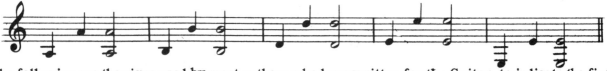

The following are the signs used by most authors who have written for the Guitar, to indicate the fingering, and which are adopted in this work.

### THE LEFT HAND.

o. Open string; 1, first finger; 2, second finger; 3, third finger; 4, little finger.

### THE RIGHT HAND.

. First finger; .. second finger; ... third finger; ✕ or + thumb.

### THE POSITIONS.

There are as many position as there are frets on the Finger board. It is the 1st finger that determines the position in which the hand is; thus, when the 1st finger is placed on the 1st fret, the hand is in the 1st position, and so on with the other positions.

# SCALE SHOWING THE NOTES, AND THE EXTENT OF THE FIRST POSITION.

The figures placed over the notes indicate the fingers of the left hand, and also the frets on which they are to be placed. The open strings are indicated by 0, the 1st finger and 1st fret by 1, the 2d finger and 2d fret by 2, the 3d finger and 3d fret by 3, and the 4th finger and 4th fret by 4. The fingers of the right hand are indicated by × for the thumb; •first finger; •• second finger; ••• third finger.

## NATURAL POSITION.

## EXERCISES IN THE 1st POSITION.

## SCALE WITH SHARPS.

## SCALE WITH FLATS.

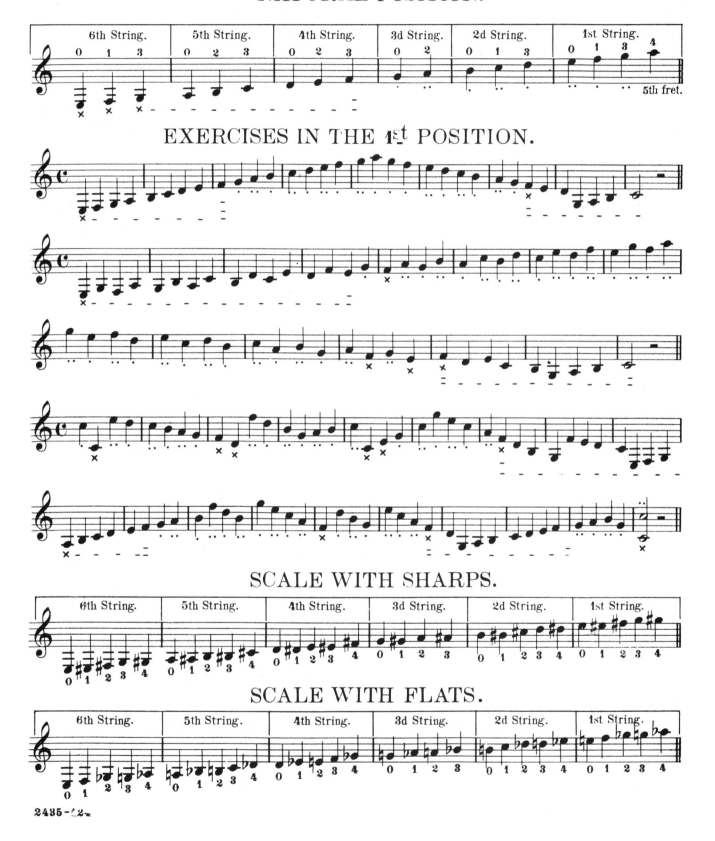

# EXERCISE WITH SHARPS AND FLATS.

# THE CHORDS.

The union of two or more notes played simultaneously is called a Chord. If the chord to be played is composed of three notes, no matter on which strings they are to be played with the thumb, 1st and 2d fingers; if composed of four notes, the 3d finger must be added; if of five or six notes, the thumb must play the two or three lowest notes by sliding from one string to the other, and the fingers take the three other strings. That all the notes of a chord may sound well, it is necessary that the fingers of the left hand should be curved to act as hammers, be pressed on the strings near the frets, and without affecting the vibration of the other strings; the fingers of the right hand should be placed against the strings intended to be struck, and not to be moved but to put the strings in motion. Chords are always divided, or played in Arpeggios; thus: the notes are played one after the other, from the lowest to the highest, but sufficiently quick to produce the effect of their being struck together.

# EXAMPLES.

In slow movements the chords are played, or arpeggioed slowly, in character with the movement, which is often indicated by this ⸳, and which is placed before the chord. In quick movements, which are to be played with energy, and require much sound from the Guitar, the same sign is used to indicate that the thumb must be slid rapidly and with force across the strings which from the chord.

The Barrer is made by pressing the 1st finger on two or more strings, on the same fret. There are two Barrérs, the Great and the Small. In the small Barrer, the first finger stops but two or three strings. In the great Barrer, the first fingr stops the whole of the six strings. To do the great barrer with ease, it is necessary to raise the wrist, and to place the thumb entirely behind the Neck.

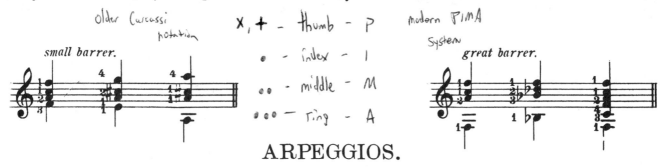

## ARPEGGIOS.

An Arpeggio is a number of notes played successively in uniform order, and which, when united, form chords. Arpeggios are used on the Guitar because they produce an agreeable effect on the instrument, and as studies, they give strength and agility to the right hand. To execute the arpeggio well, before making the strings vibrate, the fingers of the left hand should be placed at once on the notes forming the chord on which the arpeggio is to be played; and when the last note of the arpeggio is struck, the fingers should be raised to pass to the next chord. This rule is indispensable; if the fingers were to quit the notes as soon as they are struck, the vibration of the entire chord would be obstructed; of which each note is an essential part. The fingers of the right hand should not touch the strings, but to make them vibrate; with exception of the thumb, as described on page 2.

## ARPEGGIOS WITH THREE AND FOUR FINGERS.

These Arpeggios are given for the purpose of exercising the right hand, and to establish general rules, which will serve to show the fingering of that hand in all similar passages. Each Arpeggio ought to be repeated several times in succession and as soon as the pupil is able to execute several with ease, he may undertake the study of the eight Arpeggios on page 19, without however abandoning the study of these. The chords written at the top, are those from which the 22 following Arpeggios are derived.

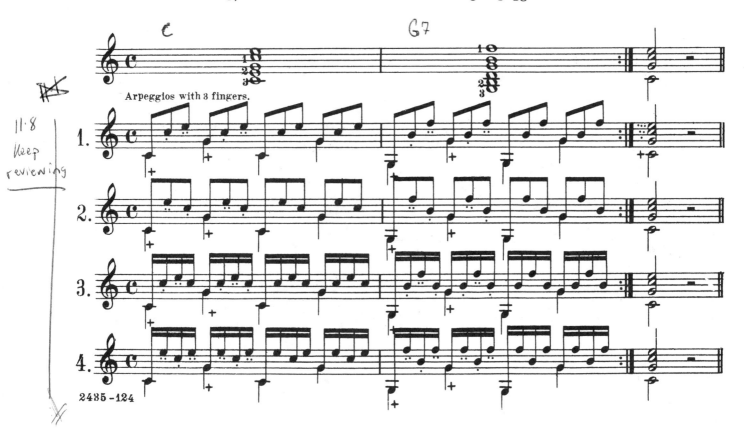

2435-124

14

Arpeggios with 4 fingers.

The thumb gliding on the first two notes.

15. With three fingers.

16. With four fingers.

The thumb gliding from one string to the other.

To facilitate the study of the eight following Arpeggios, and the execution of the left hand I have written on an upper stave over each bar, the chord which is to be played Arpeggio, as written on the stave below. The pupil will see at a glance, the chord composing the Arpeggio, and on which notes the fingers must be placed. The curved lines from one chord to the other, serve to show that the fingering of these notes has not changed, and that the fingers which press them must remain unmoved.

12-10 – tighten up timing

slow down!

even tempo

watch bass notes

don't move when you don't have to

- watch key
- watch fingerings

small barrer.

*Keep thumb down where it belongs
(right hand)

(triplet)
Count   1 + ah 2 + ah 3 + ah 4 + ah, etc.

*Right Hand Form. Keep your wrist off the bridge
• Keep a healthy break angle
to your wrist

left
hand   * Keep your 4th finger
           over the fretboard

The Guitar may be played in all keys, but, like all other instruments, it has some keys more favorable to it than others. Those which are more suitable, C major; G major, D major and minor, A major and minor, E major and minor and F major. The other keys are difficult, because they require too often, the use of the Barrér. I have therefore placed in the first part of this work, the Scales, Cadences, and Exercises only in those keys most in use. As I think it important however, to be acquainted with all the keys, and that they should be practised, I have placed in the latter part of this method all that I have thought necessary for this purpose.

# SCALES, CADENCES, EXERCISES, AND PRELUDES.

To facilitate the execution of the scales, it is necessary that the fingers of the left hand should be held sufficiently separated, and so placed that they may be put on, and taken off the strings, without moving the hand. A finger which is placed on a note, should not be moved but to finger the note following, unless this note should be an open string. In scales ascending, when passing from one note to another, the finger must not be raised too quickly from the string, lest it vibrate if left. In the following preludes and little pieces, care must be taken to sustain the notes, as well in the bass, as in the other parts, this caution is necessary, in order to obtain a full and harmonious style.

## KEY OF C MAJOR.

# KEY OF G MAJOR.

**24**

# KEY OF D MAJOR.

To facilitate the fingering in the Scale of D Major, it is necessary to advance the left hand to the second fret.

When two notes which are to be played on the same string meet, the upper note must be taken as usual, and the lower one on the next string.

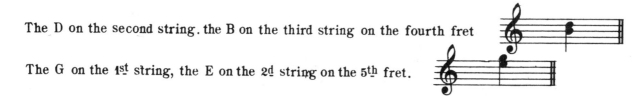

The D on the second string. the B on the third string on the fourth fret

The G on the 1st string, the E on the 2d string on the 5th fret.

**Waltz.**

**Fine.**

**D.S.**

**Rondo.**

**Fine.**

**D.S.**

*4th finger over the board*

C-24

# KEY OF A MAJOR.

March.

Allegretto.

Fine.

2435-124

# KEY OF E MAJOR.

RONDO.
Allegretto.

Waltz.

continue.

# KEY OF F MAJOR.

MARCH.
Maestoso.

Allegretto.

# KEY OF A MINOR.

# KEY OF E MINOR.

# KEY OF D MINOR.

**36**

Guitar music almost always requires several parts. which increases the difficulty of execution, unless the pupil has already acquired the habit of moving each finger of the left hand, separately and independently. The following 22 exercises are very useful in obtaining this object. Each of them should be repeated five or six times. Whilst the pupil is practising these exercises, he may at the same time apply himself to the first twelve numbers of 50 exercise page 74, and afterwards to the exercises of the Slur etc. page 38.

Continue with the same finger of the right hand.

# THE SLUR.

Two or more notes placed successively, of which only the first is made to vibrate by the right hand, and the others by the mere pressure of the fingers of the left hand, are called slurred notes. Slurs are performed both in rising and in descending. To execute slurs of two notes, in rising the lower note is to be played, and the finger of the left hand descends like a hammer and with a good deal of force upon the higher note, which must sound from the mere impulse of the finger. In descending, the higher note is played, and drawing the finger which pressed it a little to one side, so as to touch the string a little, the lower note is made to sound. If the latter note is not on an open string, it must be prepared before the higher note is made to vibrate. The slur is indicated by this sign ⌒ placed over the notes which are to be slurred.

## SLURS OF TWO NOTES RISING AND DESCENDING.

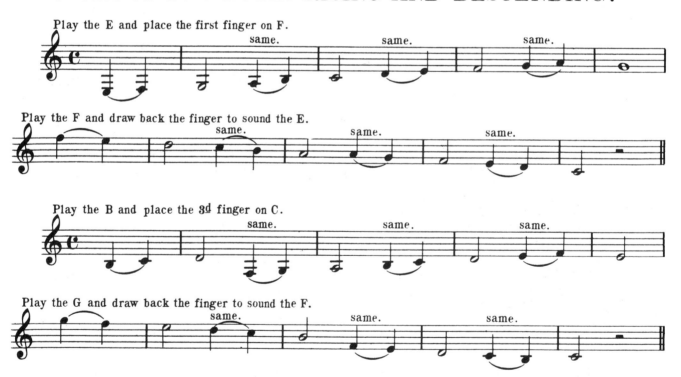

There are also slurs of two notes, descending, on two different strings, which are called "Vibration Slurs" To perform them, play the higher note, which in this case is almost always open, then strike hard with finger of the left hand the note which is to be slurred, and which will be sounded by the mere impulse of the finger.

In rising the **effect** of the slur is also produced by sliding the thumb of the right hand from one string to the other; in this case the first note must be struck rather hard and the thumb slide with **delicacy** over the next string.

Slurs of three or four notes are made in the same manner as those of two notes, by setting the first note in vibration with the right hand, and laying on or withdrawing, according as the slur is ascending or descending as many fingers of the left hand as there are notes to be slurred.

## SLURS OF THREE NOTES.

Snap the E, and then place successively the first fingher upon the F, and the third upon the G.

Snap the G, and successively remove the fingers to produce the F, and the E.

## SLURS OF FOUR NOTES.

Scales, too, may be executed in slurred notes, ascending or descending, by a mere sliding of the thumb. In this scale you set the open string to vibrating, with the thumb, letting it slide from string to string.

In this last you snap the first note and slur all the rest,

Double notes may be slurred, but only two by two.

# THE SLIDE.

The Slide is performed by one finger of the left hand, which slides along the neck in passing over all the frets from the 1st to the 2nd note, after having struck with the right hand the first of the two notes.

The slide produces a good effect on the guitar, because it imitates the sound of the voice. It is indicated by this sign.⌒

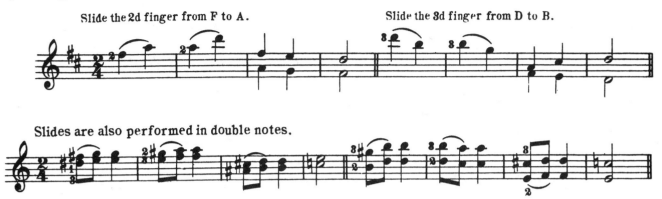

Slide the 2d finger from F to A.          Slide the 3d finger from D to B.

Slides are also performed in double notes.

## SMALL NOTES OR APPOGGIATURA.

This name is given to a small note, which sometimes is of half the value of the note which it precedes.

In this case it is the long Appoggiatura, and when it has but a very short duration it is called the short Appoggiatura. To distinguish the short from the long Appoggiatura, the former is crossed at the end.

The small notes are played the same as slurs, giving an impulse to the small note with the right hand, and making the principal note sound with the finger of the left hand.

When a common note, preceded by a small note, is accompanied by one or more parts, the small note must be played with the accompanying parts, and the principal note be slurred immediately.

Long small notes.          Small small notes.

Written.

Played.

Small notes to be played with the notes of Accompaniment.

Written.

Played.

# DOUBLE SMALL NOTES OR APPOGGIATURAS.

Two Appoggiaturas are executed in the same manner as two principal notes slurred; only with more rapidity, since the latter receive their full value, whereas the small notes borrow somewhat from the duration of the principal notes.

## SHORT PIECES FOR THE PRACTICE OF APPOGGIATURES.

Moderato.

Andantino.

# THE GRUPPETTO.

This is the name of a group of appoggiatura notes, composed of the principal note and its auxiliary note immediately above and below. It is indicated and performed in three ways.

**1.** By beginning with the principal note, A(♪ ∾.) **2.** By beginning with the auxiliary above,(B ∾.)

**3.** By beginning with the auxiliary below,(C ∾.) This is called inverted in most treatises,and indicated(**S.**)

## EXAMPLE.

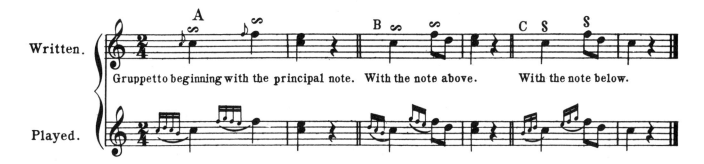

If a little note of the gruppetto is to be altered by a Sharp or Flat, it is thus indicated for the auxiliary above,(♭∾.) and thus for the auxiliary below.(∾♯.)

When the Gruppetto stands between two principal notes, it is always commenced with the upper auxiliary.

# THE TRILL.

The Trill is where a note alternates, for a longer or shorter time, according to its value, and very rapidly, with the note which is a tone or half a tone above it, and which is termed the auxiliary note. The Trill should generally begin and end with the principal note. Every Trill should have a termination; this termination consists of the tone or semitone below, followed by the principal note. (See following Examples.)

On the Guitar the trill is made in three ways: **1.** By snapping the first note, and slurring the rest of the Trill. **2.** By snapping the principal, and slurring the auxiliary note. **3.** By taking the two notes upon two different strings with the left hand, and snapping them with two or three fingers.

When the short duration of the note on which the Trill is made, or when the following note prevents a termination, it is no longer a *Trill,* but merely a *note trilled*.

This ornament is a fragment of a Trill. It is made upon long and short notes; but has a particularly fine effect upon the latter; it is indicated by the sign.〰

## MUFFLED TONES.

To damp or smother the sounds, you have only to place the fingers of the right hand upon the strings just snapped, after allowing them to vibrate during their written value, (which is here a sixteenth.) Chords of five or six notes are stopped by laying the palm of the right hand upon all the strings, near the rosette.

# POSITIONS.

There are twelve positions on the finger-board of the Guitar; among those there are five which are called principal positions, as they are most in use, and a knowledge of them is sufficient to get acquainted with the others. These positions are the 1st, 4th, 5th, 7th, and 9th. The study of the Scale, of the exercises and the following pieces, in those different positions, will be sufficient for this purpose.

## SCALE IN FOURTH POSITION.

# SCALE IN THE FIFTH POSITION.

# SCALE IN THE SEVENTH POSITION.

# SCALE IN THE NINTH POSITION.

There are cases where we profit by a note played upon an open string, to pass with greater facility from one position to another; this note is indicated by a (○) which is placed over a note.

Sometimes the first finger is drawn back one fret, without the position of the hand being altered on that account.

The four following pieces are written so that the pupil may go through the different positions.

# DOUBLE NOTES.

On the Guitar there are passages of double notes or third, sixths, octaves, and tenths; to facilitate their execution, it is necessary to slide the fingers as much as possible, in passing from one fret to another. In these first exercises the fingers which are to slide are marked by small lines placed between the numbers, to indicate the fingering of the left hand.

## SCALE IN THIRDS.

## SCALE IN SIXTHS.

## SCALE IN OCTAVES.

## SCALE IN TENTHS.

Study.
Andante.

In passages of thirds, sixths, and tenths, sometimes we find an accompanying part which rests upon a single continuous note, and which is put in to produce an effect peculiar to the guitar. This part should always be executed upon an open string, even if the other parts are higher, in which case they should be taken upon strings below the open string.

# EXAMPLE.

in the Major and Minor Keys, which have not been presented in the First Part.

## KEY OF B MINOR.

## KEY OF F♯ MINOR.

## KEY OF C♯ MINOR.

# KEY OF B MAJOR.

# KEY OF G SHARP MINOR.

63

**Exercise.**

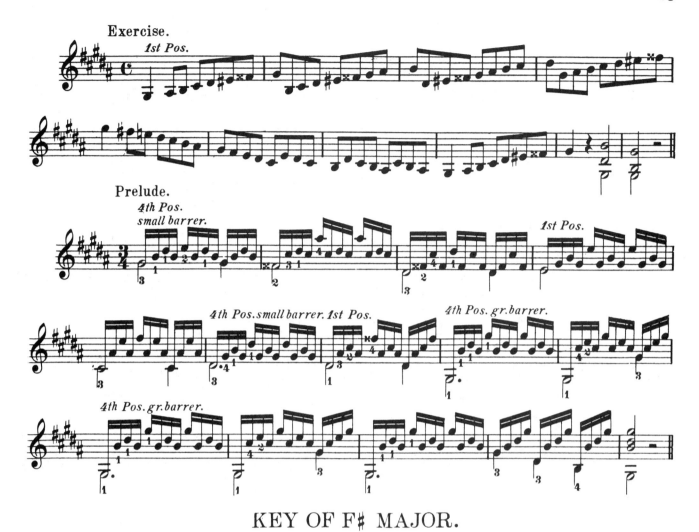

## KEY OF F♯ MAJOR.

Serving also for that of G♭ Major with six flats.

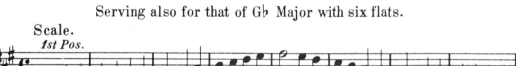

Cadence.

Exercise

2435-124

KEY OF D♯ MINOR.

# KEY OF B♭ MAJOR.

# KEY OF G MINOR.

**Prelude.**

## KEY OF Eb MAJOR.

**Scale.**

**Cadence**

**Exercise.**

**Prelude.**

## KEY OF C MINOR.

**Scale.**

## KEY OF A♭ MAJOR.

**Prelude.**

# KEY OF F MINOR.

**Scale.**

**Cadence.**

**Exercise.**

**Prelude.**

# KEY OF Db MAJOR.

Serving also for that of C♯ Major, with seven sharps.

**Scale.**

**Cadence.**

## KEY OF B♭ MINOR.

# HARMONICS.

Harmonics are produced by placing a finger of the left hand across all the strings of the Guitar at certain divisions of the finger board. The finger must press lightly, yet with sufficient force to prevent the string from vibrating as if open. As soon as the string has been struck with sufficient force near to the bridge, the finger must be taken off. Harmonics sound an octave higher than what they are marked. They are produced at the 12th, 7th, 5th, 4th and 3d fret, as the following table shows.

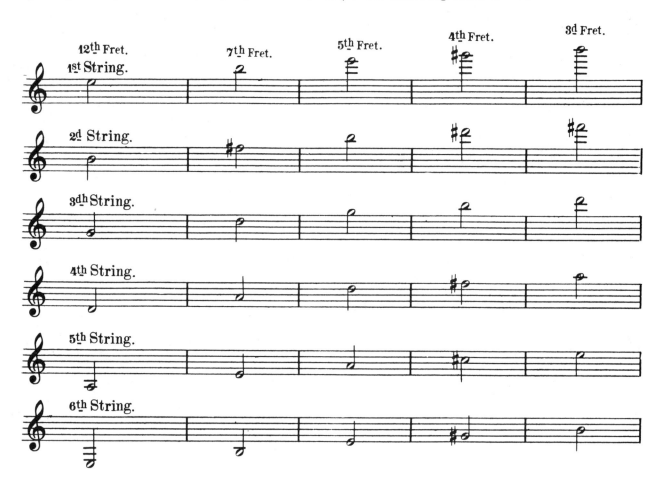

## EXERCISE IN HARMONICS.

The upper figures point out the frets, and the lower ones the strings.

All the notes within the compass of the Guitar may be played harmonically. To do the note which is to be played harmonically is fingered in the same manner as an ordinary note; then the point of the forefinger of the right hand is placed at the 12th fret distant from the note which before has been fingered by the left hand, the thumb is then removed from the forefinger, which presses lightly on the string, and strikes this string which will produce a harmonic sound.

### Allegretto.

Position of the left hand

Place where the 1st finger of the right hand must successively be played.

### RONDO TO EXERCISE ALL THE POSITIONS.

Moderato.

2435-124

## 50 EXERCISES PROGRESSING IN DIFFICULTY.

76

78

82

Caprice.

16.

March.

17.

2435-124

RONDO.

Allegretto.

21.

Sicilian.

22.

MAJOR.

Fine.

D.S.

Moderato.

23.

88

RONDO.
Allegretto.

29.

Chase.

30.

Larghetto.

31.

MARCH.

32.

RONDO.

Allegretto.

33.

Waltz

34.

March.

39.

Fine.

98

AIR SUISSE.

Allegro.

42.

Von Weber's Waltz
Andante.

43.

VAR.

D.C.

AIR ITALIAN.
Andantino.

44.

VAR I

VAR II.

9th Pos.

Tempo I.

dolce.

9th Pos.

Duke de Reichstadt's Waltz.

45.

To excute the following pieces, the Guitar must be tuned in E Major.

MARCH

48.

## EXPLANATION OF THE SIGNS.

### IN ORDER TO EXECUTE THE TWO FOLLOWING PIECES.

FRISER.— Indicates that the fingers of the right hand are to be kept closed, with the exception of the thumb; and opened one after another, letting them pass over all the strings without any movement of the arm.

POUCE.— The thumb of the right hand must be passed lightly over all the strings. INDEX.— Pass the index finger of the right hand very lightly from the highest to the lowest string, quite close to the rosette.

VIBRATION.— Let the fingers of the left hand fall in hammer fashion, upon the notes so designated, with force enough to set the strings vibrating, without pinching or snapping them. TAMBOUR.— Strike with the thumb of the right hand upon all the strings near the bridge, with force enough but without hardness.

# AGATHA POLKA.

GUITAR SOLO
No **217**.

M. Carcassi.
7th pos.

18099-1
2435-124

*Copyright 1890 by Carl Fischer, New York.*

# HERMOSE POLKA.

M. Carcassi.

# AZELIA POLKA.

GUITAR SOLO
No **219**.

M. Carcassi.

For this Polka the 6th string must be put down one tone (D)

7th position.

18097-1
2435-124

D.C.

GUITAR SOLO
Nº **220**.

# HERMINA POLKA.

Matteo Carcassi.

INTR.
Allegro.

POLKA.

18,096-
2435-124

# Melody

A. RUBINSTEIN
Arr. by C. J. DORN.

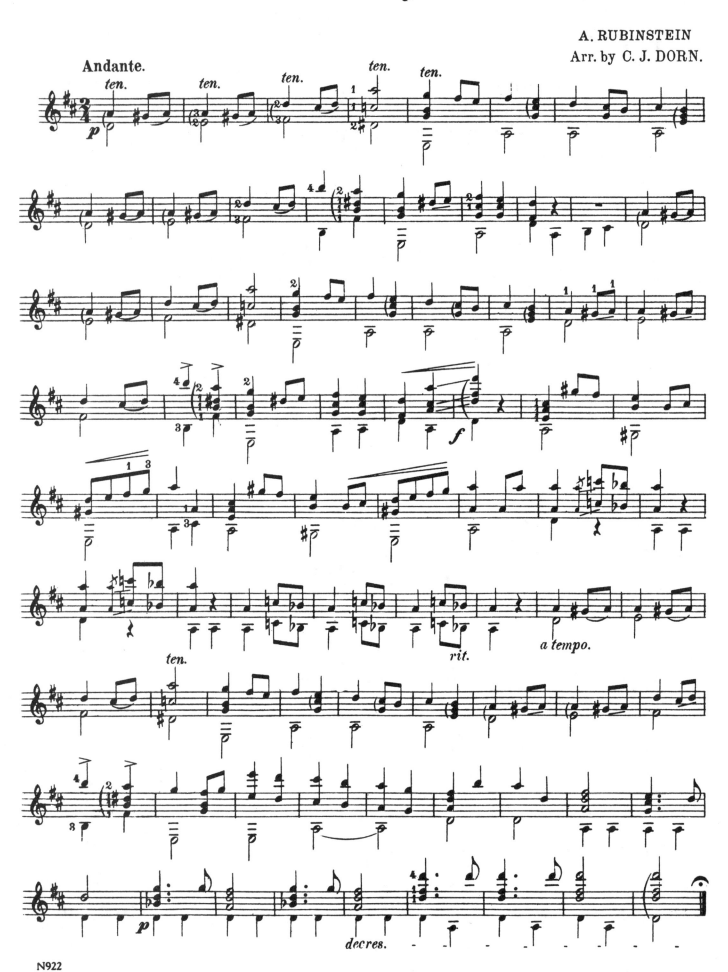

N922

# Consolation
## Song without words

F. MENDELSSOHN
Op 30, No. 3
arr. by J. S. COLLINS.

Adagio non troppo.

O thumb of left hand.
Signs: 1 = 1st finger.
2 = 2nd finger etc.

In chords of five notes use the little finger of right hand to pick with.
All chords not marked staccato, should be played running or arpeggio, the
mark 𝄎 is omitted to avoid confusion.

N922

WALTZ.

**Guitar I.**

**Guitar II.**

WALTZ.

I

II

GALOP

**WALTZ.**

REICHELT.

1st Guitar with Capo d'Astro in the 3rd Position.

2d Guitar without Capo d'Astro.

**GALOP.**

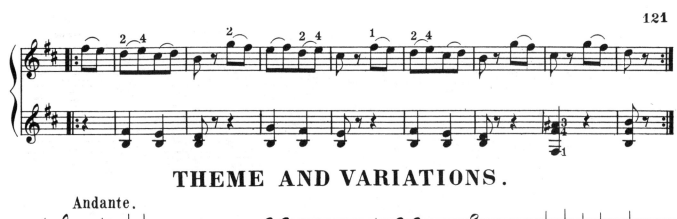

# THEME AND VARIATIONS.

122

VAR. III.
Tempo di Marcia.

VAR. IV.
Alla Polacca.

VAR. V.
Tempo di Vaise.

2435-124

POLONAISE.

# Auld Lang Syne.

(So lang her.)

arr. by W. J. Kitchener.

# Home, sweet Home.

## (Süsse Heimat.)

arr. by W. J. Kitchener.

Mid plea - - sures and pa - - la - ces though we may roam, be it ev - - er so hum - ble there's no place like home! A char - mer from the skies seems to hal - low us there, which seek through the world, is ne'er met with else - where Home! Home! sweet sweet Home! there's no place like Home! there's no place like Home!

# Kate Kearney.

arr. by W. J. Kitchener.

# Annie Laurie.

arr. by W. J. Kitchener.

# Hail Columbia.

arr. by W. J. Kitchener.

Allegro maestoso.

Hail - Co - lum - bia hap-py land! Hail ye he - roes! heav'n-born band, who fought and bled in free - dom's cause, who fought and bled in free - dom's cause. And when the storm of war was gone, en - joyed the peace your val - or won. Let In - de - pen - dence be your boast ev - er mind-ful what it cost. Ev - er grate-ful for the prize, let its al - tar reach the skies. Firm u - ni - ted let us be, rally - ing round our li - ber - ty! As a band of broth - ers join'd peace and safe - ty we shall find.

3653-22

# GLOSSARY

A . . . . . . . . . . .to, in or at; *a tempo*, in time
*Accelerando (accel.)*.Gradually increasing the speed
*Accent* . . . . . . . .Emphasis on certain parts of the measure
*Adagio* . . . . . . . .Slowly leisurely
*Ad libitum (ad lib.)*.At pleasure; not in strict time
*A due (a 2)*. . . . . .To be played by both instruments
*Agitato* . . . . . . .Restless, with agitation
*Al or Alla*. . . . . .In the style of
*Alla Marcia* . . . . .In the style of a March
*Allegretto*. . . . . .Diminutive of allegro; moderately fast, lively; faster than *andante;* slower than *allegro*
*Allegro* . . . . . . .Lively; brisk, rapid.
*Allegro assai* . . . .Very rapidly
*Amoroso* . . . . . . .Affectionately
*Andante* . . . . . . .In moderately slow time
*Andantino* . . . . . .Diminutive of *andante;* strictly *slower* than andante, but often used in the reverse sense
*Anima, con* } . . . .With animation
*Animato* }
*A piacere*. . . . . . .At pleasure; equivalent to *ad libitum*
*Appassionato*. . . . .Impassioned
*Arpeggio* . . . . . . .A broken chord
*Assai* . . . . . . . .Very; *Allegro assai*, very rapidly
*A tempo* . . . . . . .In the original tempo
*Attacca* . . . . . . .Attack or begin what follows without pausing
*Barcarolle* . . . . . .A Venetian boatman's song
*Bis* . . . . . . . . .Twice, repeat the passage
*Bravura* . . . . . . .Brilliant; bold; spirited
*Brillante* . . . . . .Showy, sparkling, brilliant
*Brio, con* . . . . . .With much spirit
*Cadenza* . . . . . . .An elaborate, florid passage introduced as an embellishment
*Cantabile*. . . . . . .In a singing style
*Canzonetta* . . . . . .A short song or air
*Capriccio a* . . . . .At pleasure, ad libitum
*Cavatina* . . . . . . .An air, shorter and simpler than the aria, and in one division, without Da Capo
*Chord* . . . . . . . .The harmony of three or more tones of different pitch produced simultaneously
*Coda* . . . . . . . . .A supplement at the end of a composition
*Col or con* . . . . . .With
*Crescendo (cresc.)*.Swelling; increasing in loudness
*Da or dal* . . . . . .From
*Da Capo (D. C.)* . . .From the beginning
*Dal Segno (D. S.)*.From the sign
*Decrescendo (decresc.)*Decreasing in strength
*Diminuendo (dim.)*.Gradually softer
*Divisi*. . . . . . . .Divided, each part to be played by a separate instrument
*Dolce (dol.)* . . . .Softly; sweetly
*Dolcissimo* . . . . . .Very sweetly and softly
*Dominant*. . . . . . .The fifth tone in the major or minor scale
*Duet or Duo* . . . . .A composition for two performers
E . . . . . . . . . . .And
*Elegante* . . . . . . .Elegant, graceful
*Energico* . . . . . . .With energy, vigorously
*Enharmonic* . . . . . .Alike in pitch, but different in notation
*Espressivo* . . . . . .With expression
*Finale* . . . . . . . .The concluding movement
*Fine* . . . . . . . . .The end
*Forte (f)* . . . . . .Loud
*Forte-piano (fp)* . .Accent strongly, diminishing instantly to piano
*Fortissimo (ff)*. . .Very loud
*Forzando (fz >)* . . .Indicates that a note or chord is to be strongly accented
*Forza* . . . . . . . .Force of tone
*Fuoco, con* . . . . . .With fire; with spirit
*Giocoso*. . . . . . . .Joyously, playfully
*Giusto* . . . . . . . .Exact; in strict time
*Grandioso*. . . . . . .Grand; pompous; majestic
*Grave* . . . . . . . .Very slow and solemn
*Grazioso* . . . . . . .Gracefully
*Harmony*. . . . . . . .In general, a combination of tones, or chords, producing music
*Key note* . . . . . . .The first degree of the scale, the tonic
*Largamente* . . . . . .Very broad in style
*Larghetto* . . . . . .Slow, but not so slow as Largo; nearly like Andantino
*Largo* . . . . . . . .Broad and slow; the slowest tempo-mark
*Legato*. . . . . . . .Smoothly, the reverse of staccato
*Ledger-line*. . . . . .A small added line above or below the staff
*Lento* . . . . . . . .Slow, between Andante and Largo
*L'istesso tempo*.In the same time, (or tempo)
*Loco*. . . . . . . . .In place. Play as written, no longer, an octave higher or lower
*Ma* . . . . . . . . . .But
*Ma non troppo*. . . . .Lively, but not too much so
*Maestoso*. . . . . . .Majestically; dignified
*Maggiore*. . . . . . .Major Key
*Marcato*. . . . . . . .Marked
*Meno* . . . . . . . . .Less
*Meno mosso* . . . . . .Less quickly
*Mezzo* . . . . . . . .Half; moderately

*Mezzo-piano (mp)* .Moderately soft
*Minore* . . . . . . . .Minor Key
*Moderato*. . . . . . .Moderately. *Allegro moderato*, moderately fast
*Molto*. . . . . . . . .Much; very
*Morendo* . . . . . . .Dying away
*Mosso*. . . . . . . . .Equivalent to rapid. *Più mosso*, quicker.
*Moto*. . . . . . . . .Motion. *Con moto*, with animation
*Non*. . . . . . . . . .Not
*Notation* . . . . . . .The art of representing musical sounds by means of written characters
*Obbligata* . . . . . .An indispensable part
*Opus (Op.)* . . . . . .A work.
*Ossia*. . . . . . . . .Or; or else. Generally indicating an easier method
*Ottava (8va)*. . . . .To be played an octave higher
*Pause (⌢)* . . . .The sign indicating a pause or rest.
*Perdendosi*. . . . . .Dying away gradually
*Piacere, a* . . . . . .At pleasure
*Pianissimo (pp)* . .Very softly
*Piano (p)* . . . . . .Softly
*Più*. . . . . . . . . .More
*Più Allegro* . . . . .More quickly
*Più tosto*. . . . . . .Quicker
*Poco or un poco* . . .A little
*Poco a poco*. . . . . .Gradually, by degrees; little by little
*Poco più mosso* . . . .A little faster
*Poco meno*. . . . . . .A little slower
*Poco più* . . . . . . .A little faster
*Poi*. . . . . . . . . .Then; afterwards
*Pomposo* . . . . . . .Pompous; grand
*Prestissimo* . . . . .As quickly as possible
*Presto (1mo)* . . . . .Very quick; faster than *Allegro*
*Primo (1mo)*. . . . . .The first
*Quartet* . . . . . . .A piece of music for four performers.
*Quasi*. . . . . . . . .As if; in the style of
*Quintet*. . . . . . . .A piece of music for five performers
*Rallentando (rall.)* Gradually slower
*Replica*. . . . . . . .Repetition. *Senza replica*, without repeats
*Rinforzando* . . . . .With special emphasis
*Ritardando (rit.)*.Gradually slower and slower
*Risoluto* . . . . . . .Resolutely; bold; energetic
*Ritenuto* . . . . . . .In slower time
*Scherzando*. . . . . .Playfully; sportively
*Secondo (2do)* . . . .The second singer, instrumentalist or part
*Segue*. . . . . . . . .Follow on in similar style
*Semplice* . . . . . . .Simply; unaffectedly
*Senza*. . . . . . . . .Without. *Senza sordino* without mute
*Sforzando (sf)* . . .Forcibly; with sudden emphasis
*Simile or Simili*. .In like manner
*Smorzando (smorz)* .Diminishing in sound. Equivalent to *Morendo*
*Solo*. . . . . . . . .For one performer only. *Soli*; for all
*Sordino*. . . . . . . .A mute. *Con sordino*, with the mute
*Sostenuto*. . . . . . .Sustained; prolonged
*Sotto*. . . . . . . . .Below; under. *Sotto voce*, in a subdued tone
*Spirito*. . . . . . . .Spirit. *con Spirito* with spirit
*Staccato*. . . . . . .Detached; separate
*Stentando* . . . . . .Dragging or retarding the tempo
*Stretto or stretta*.An increase of speed. *Più stretto* faster
*Subdominant* . . . . .The fourth tone in the diatonic scale
*Syncopation* . . . . .Change of accent from a strong beat to a weak one
*Tacet*. . . . . . . . ."Is silent" Signified that an instrument or vocal part, so marked, is omitted during the movement or number in question.
*Tempo*. . . . . . . . .Movement; rate of speed.
*Tempo primo* . . . . .Return to the original tempo.
*Tenuto (ten.)* . . . .Held for the full value.
*Thema or Theme* . .The subject or melody.
*Tonic*. . . . . . . . .The key-note of any scale.
*Tranquillo* . . . . . .Quietly.
*Tremolando, Tremolo* A tremulous fluctuation of tone.
*Trio* . . . . . . . . .A piece of music for three performers.
*Triplet* . . . . . . .A group of three notes to be performed in the time of two of equal value in the regular rhythm.
*Troppo* . . . . . . . .Too; too much. *Allegro, ma non troppo*, not too quickly.
*Tutti* . . . . . . . .All; all the instruments.
*Un*. . . . . . . . . .A, one, an.
*Una corda* . . . . . .On one string.
*Variatione* . . . . . .The transformation of a melody by means of harmonic, rhythmic and melodic changes and embellishments.
*Veloce* . . . . . . . .Quick, rapid, swift.
*Vibrato* . . . . . . .A wavering tone-effect, which should be sparingly used.
*Vivace* . . . . . . . .With vivacity; bright; spirited.
*Vivo*. . . . . . . . .Lively; spirited
*Volti Subito V. S.* .Turn over quickly.